THE
BLUE
BOOK

C000110094

Three Chord Tricks

Wise Publications
London/New York/Paris/Sydney/Copenhagen/Madrid

Also available...

Three Chord Tricks: The Red Book
Twenty-two more hit songs...

Amazing Grace Judy Collins
Blowin' In The Wind Bob Dylan
Brimful Of Asha Cornershop
C'mon Everybody Eddie Cochran
El Condor Pasa (If I Could) Simon & Garfunkel
Eleanor Rigby The Beatles
Free To Decide The Cranberries
Going Down The Stone Roses
Johnny B Goode Chuck Berry
Long Tall Sally Little Richard
Me And Julio Down By The Schoolyard Paul Simon
Mr Tambourine Man Bob Dylan/The Byrds
Mull Of Kintyre Wings
Oh Boy Buddy Holly
Paperback Writer The Beatles
Ride A White Swan T Rex
Rock Around The Clock Bill Haley and His Comets
Spice Up Your Life Spice Girls
Still Water The Four Tops
The First Cut Is The Deepest Cat Stevens/Rod Stewart
The Mighty Quinn Bob Dylan/Manfred Mann
Walk Of Life Dire Straits
Order No. AM951380

Exclusive Distributors:
Music Sales Limited
8-9 Frith Street,
London W1V 5TZ, England.
Music Sales Pty Limited
120 Rothschild Avenue,
Rosebery, NSW 2018,
Australia.

Order No. AM951379
ISBN 0-7119-7241-9
This book © Copyright 1998 by Wise Publications

Compiled by Peter Evans
Music arranged by Rikky Rooksby
Music processed by The Pitts
Cover design by Studio Twenty, London

Printed in the United Kingdom by
Caligraving Limited, Thetford, Norfolk.

Your Guarantee of Quality
As publishers, we strive to produce every book to the
highest commercial standards.
This book has been carefully designed to minimise awkward
page turns and to make playing from it a real pleasure.
Particular care has been given to specifying acid-free,
neutral-sized paper made from pulps which have not been
elemental chlorine bleached. This pulp is from farmed
sustainable forests and was produced with special regard
for the environment.
Throughout, the printing and binding have been planned
to ensure a sturdy, attractive publication which should
give years of enjoyment.
If your copy fails to meet our high standards, please
us and we will gladly replace it.

Music Sales' complete catalogue describes thousands of
titles and is available in full colour sections by subject,
direct from Music Sales Limited. Please state your areas
of interest and send a cheque/postal order for £1.50
for postage to: Music Sales Limited, Newmarket Road,
Bury St. Edmunds, Suffolk IP33 3YB.

The Three Chord Trick songbooks
allow even the beginner guitarist to build
a repertoire of rock classics.
Simply by mastering the three chords used in any of these
songs, you really could play in a day...perhaps even less!
And once you know them, you're on the way to being a
fully-fledged performer.
This songbook doesn't use musical notation, instead you just
learn three easy-to-read chord boxes.
Many popular songs only use three chords.
The most common formula is the 'three-chord trick',
using the three primary chords of any major key.
So in G this would be G, C, and D.
Many rock'n'roll numbers and Dylan's folk-inspired
songs use only these chords.

Three Chord Tricks

Throughout the book chord boxes are printed at the
head of each song; the chord changes are shown
above the lyrics. It's left up to you, the guitarist,
to decide on a strum rhythm or picking pattern.
You might find the pitch of the vocal line is not always
comfortable because it is pitched too high or too low.
In that case, you can change the key without learning
a new set of chords; simply place a capo
behind a suitable fret.
Whatever you do, this three-chord songbook
guarantees hours of enjoyment for
the prospective guitarist.

Relative Tuning

The guitar can be tuned with the aid of pitch pipes or dedicated electronic guitar tuners which are available through your local music dealer. If you do not have a tuning device, you can use relative tuning. Estimate the pitch of the 6th string as near as possible to E or at least a comfortable pitch (not too high, as you might break other strings in tuning up). Then, while checking the various positions on the diagram, place a finger from your left hand on the:

5th fret of the E or 6th string and **tune the open A** (or 5th string) to the note (A)

5th fret of the A or 5th string and **tune the open D** (or 4th string) to the note (D)

5th fret of the D or 4th string and **tune the open G** (or 3rd string) to the note (G)

4th fret of the G or 3rd string and **tune the open B** (or 2nd string) to the note (B)

5th fret of the B or 2nd string and **tune the open E** (or 1st string) to the note (E)

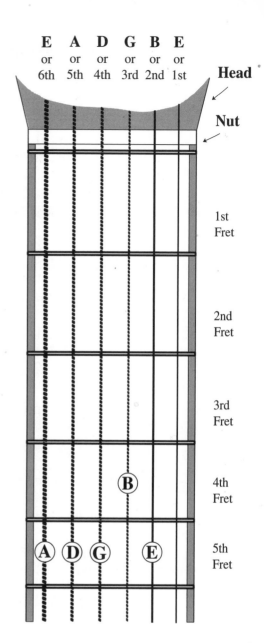

Reading Chord Boxes

Chord boxes are diagrams of the guitar neck viewed head upwards, face on as illustrated. The top horizontal line is the nut, unless a higher fret number is indicated, the others are the frets.

The vertical lines are the strings, starting from E (or 6th) on the left to E (or 1st) on the right.

The black dots indicate where to place your fingers.

Strings marked with an O are played open, not fretted.

Strings marked with an X should not be played.

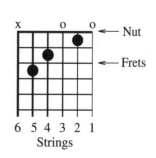

Achy Breaky Heart

Words & Music by Don Von Tress

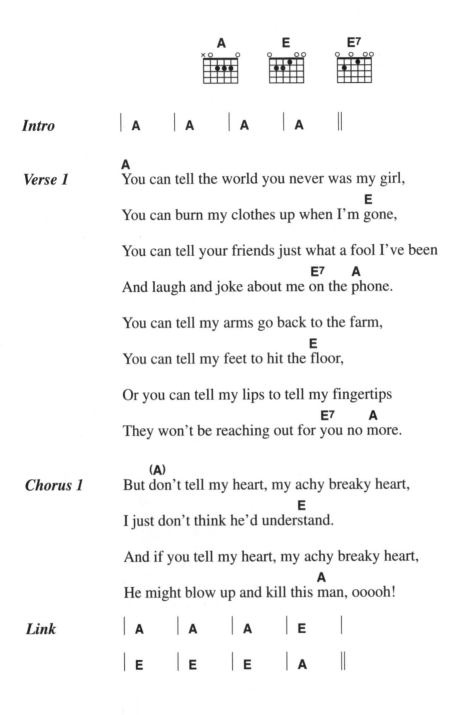

Intro | A | A | A | A ‖

Verse 1
A
You can tell the world you never was my girl,
                                        E
You can burn my clothes up when I'm gone,

You can tell your friends just what a fool I've been
                              E⁷   A
And laugh and joke about me on the phone.

You can tell my arms go back to the farm,
                              E
You can tell my feet to hit the floor,

Or you can tell my lips to tell my fingertips
                                    E⁷   A
They won't be reaching out for you no more.

Chorus 1
            (A)
But don't tell my heart, my achy breaky heart,
                              E
I just don't think he'd understand.

And if you tell my heart, my achy breaky heart,
                              A
He might blow up and kill this man, ooooh!

Link | A | A | A | E |

| E | E | E | A ‖

Verse 2

         A
You can tell your Ma I moved to Arkansas,

                   E
You can tell your dog to bite my leg.

Or tell your brother Cliff whose fist can tell my lip

          E⁷   **A**
He never really liked me anyway,

Or tell your Aunt Louise, tell anything you please,

             E
Myself already knows I'm not okay,

Or you can tell my eyes to watch out for my mind,

          E⁷   **A**
It might be walking out on me today.

Chorus 2   As Chorus 1

Instrumental | A | A | A | E |

                 | E | E | E | A ||

Chorus 3   As Chorus 1

                 N.C
Chorus 4   But don't tell my heart, my achy breaky heart,

             I just don't think he'd understand.

             And if you tell my heart, my achy breaky heart,

             He might blow up and kill this man, ooooh!

Instrumental ||: A | A | A | E |

                 | E | E | E | A :|| *Repeat to fade*

All Along The Watchtower

Words & Music by Bob Dylan

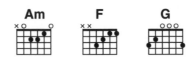

Verse 1

Am   F   G
"There must be some way out of here,"

Am   F   G
Said the joker to the thief,

Am   F   G
"There's too much confusion,

Am   F G
I can't get no relief.

Am   F   G
Business men, they drink my wine,

Am   F   G
Ploughmen dig my earth,

Am   F   G
None of them along the line

Am   F   G
Know what any of it is worth."

Verse 2

Am   F   G
"No reason to get excited,"

Am   F   G
The thief he kindly spoke,

Am   F   G
"There are many here among us

Am   F G
Who feel that life is but a joke.

Am   F   G
But you and I we've been through that,

Am   F   G
And this is not our fate,

Am   F   G
So let us not talk falsely now,

Am   F   G
The hour is getting late."

Verse 3

```
         Am          F              G
         All along the watchtower,
         Am            F     G
         Princes kept the view
         Am              F              G
         While other women came and went,
         Am            F    G
         Barefoot servants, too.
         Am           F         G
         Outside in the distance
         Am           F    G
         A wildcat did growl,
         Am              F          G
         Two riders were approaching,
         Am              F      G   Am
         The wind began to howl.
```

All Right Now

Words & Music by Paul Rodgers & Andy Fraser

A **D** **G**

Intro ‖: A D | A | G D | A :‖

Verse 1

       A   **D A**
There she stood in the street
G   **D**   **A**
Smiling from her head to her feet,
            D A
I said, "Hey, what is this?
            G   **D**   **A**
Now baby, maybe, maybe she's in need of a kiss,"
            D **A**
I said, "Hey, what's your name, baby?
G   **D**   **A**
Maybe we can see things the same,
            D A
Now don't you wait or   hesitate,
      G   **D**   **A**
Let's move before they raise the parking rate."

Chorus 1

A   **G**
All right now,
        D   **A**
Baby it's all right now.
A   **G**
All right now,
        D   **A**
Baby it's all right now.

Verse 2

```
            A        D  A
I took her home to my place
G            D         A
Watching every move on her face,
                D           A
She said, "Look, what's your game baby,
G             D         A
Are you trying to put me in shame?"
                D    A
I said, "Slow, don't go so fast,
G               D         A
Don't you think that love can last?"
                D    A
She said, "Love – Lord above!
G                 D         A
Now you're trying to trick me in love."
```

Chorus 2

```
A          G
All right now,
          D       A
Baby it's all right now.
A          G
All right now,
          D       A
Baby it's all right now.


‖: A        G
   All right now,
          D       A
Baby it's all right now.
A          G
All right now,
          D       A
Baby it's all right now.  :‖   *Repeat to fade*
```

Big Yellow Taxi

Words & Music by Joni Mitchell

A **B7** **E**

Intro
| A | A | B7 | B7 |

| E | E | E | E |

Verse 1
      A   E
They paved paradise and put up a parking lot
     A   B7   E
With a pink hotel, a boutique and a swinging hot-spot.

Chorus 1
E
Don't it always seem to go
     A   E
That you don't know what you've got till it's gone.
     A   B7   E
They paved paradise, put up a parking lot.
(E)
Choo ba ba ba ba,

Choo ba ba ba ba.

Verse 2
     A   E
They took all the trees and put them in a tree museum
     A   B7   E
And they charged all the people a dollar and a half just to see 'em.

Chorus 2   As Chorus 1

Verse 3
A   E
Hey farmer farmer, put away that DDT now,
     A   B7   E
Give me spots on apples but leave me the birds and the bees, please!

Chorus 3   As Chorus 1

Verse 4

    A   **E**
Late last night I heard the screen door slam

    A   **B7**   **E**
And a big yellow taxi took away my old man.

Chorus 4

E
Don't it always seem to go

    A   **E**
That you don't know what you've got till it's gone.

    A   **B7**   **E**
They paved paradise, put up a parking lot.

Choo ba ba ba ba.

   E
I said, don't it always seem to go

    A   **E**
That you don't know what you've got till it's gone.

    A   **B7**   **E**
They paved paradise, put up a parking lot.

Choo ba ba ba ba.

    A   **B7**   **E**
They paved paradise, put up a parking lot.

Choo ba ba ba ba.

    A   **B7**   **E**
They paved paradise, put up a parking lot.

Brown Eyed Girl

Words & Music by Van Morrison

G   C   D

Intro   ‖: G | C | G | D :‖

Verse 1

```
G                C     G           D
Hey where did we go, days when the rains came,
G                C     G       D
Down in the hollow, playin' a new game.
G              C
Laughin' and a-runnin', hey hey,
G              D
Skipping and a-jumping
G              C                  G  D
In the misty morning fog with  our hearts a-thumping
        C  D
And you,   my brown-eyed girl,
C  D                 G  D
You,   my brown-eyed girl.
```

Verse 2

```
G             C       G              D
Whatever happened to Tuesday and so slow,
G                 C          G         D
Going down the old mine with a transistor radio,
G              C
Standing in the sunlight laughing,
G               D
Hiding behind a rainbow's wall,
G             C     G          D
Slipping and a-sliding all along the waterfall
         C  D                        G
With you,       my brown-eyed girl,
C  D             G
You,   my brown-eyed girl.
D                                    G
Do you remember when we used to sing:
```

Chorus 1

```
G        C        G        D
```
Sha la la, la la la la, la la la-la te da,

(Spoken) Just like that.
```
G        C        G        D
```
Sha la la, la la la la, la la la-la te da, la te (da.)

Link

‖ G ‖ G ‖ G ‖ G ‖ C ‖ G ‖ D ‖

da.

Verse 3

```
G        C        G        D
```
So hard to find my way now that I'm all on my own,
```
G        C        G        D
```
I saw you just the other day, my, how you have grown.
```
G        C
```
Cast my memory back there, Lord,
```
G        D
```
Sometimes I'm overcome thinkin' 'bout it,
```
G        C        G        D
```
Laughing and a-runnin' hey hey, behind the stadium
```
      C  D        G
```
With you,   my brown-eyed girl,
```
C   D        G
```
You,   my brown-eyed girl.
```
D                G
```
Do you remember when we used to sing:

Chorus 2

‖: As Chorus 1 :‖ *Repeat to fade*

Bye Bye Love

Words & Music by Felice & Boudleaux Bryant

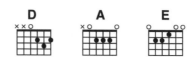

Chorus 1

D   A   D   A
Bye bye love, bye bye happiness,
D   A   E   A
Hello loneliness, I think I'm gonna cry.
D   A   D   A
Bye bye love, bye bye sweet caress,
D   A   E   A
Hello emptiness, I feel like I could die,
              E   A
Bye bye, my love, goodbye.

Verse 1

           E   A
There goes my baby with someone new,
           E   A
She sure looks happy, I sure am blue.
           D   E
She was my baby till he stepped in,
                   A
Goodbye to romance that might have been.

Chorus 2

D   A   D   A
Bye bye love, bye bye happiness,
D   A   E   A
Hello loneliness, I think I'm gonna cry.
D   A   D   A
Bye bye love, bye bye sweet caress,
D   A   E   A
Hello emptiness, I feel like I could die,
              E   A
Bye bye, my love, goodbye.

Verse 2

                 E   **A**
I'm through with romance, I'm through with love,

                 E   **A**
I'm through with counting the stars above.

            D   **E**
And here's the reason that I'm so free,

                        A
My lovin' baby is through with me.

Chorus 3

D   **A**   **D**   **A**
Bye bye love, bye bye happiness,

D   **A**   **E**   **A**
Hello loneliness, I think I'm gonna cry.

D   **A**   **D**   **A**
Bye bye love, bye bye sweet caress,

D   **A**   **E**   **A**
Hello emptiness, I feel like I could die,

               E   **A**
Bye bye, my love, goodbye.

Coda

               E   **A**
‖: Bye bye my love, goodbye.   :‖   *Repeat to fade*

Cecilia

Words & Music by Paul Simon

G   C   D

Chorus 1

G   C   G
Celia, you're breaking my heart,
        C   G   D
You're shaking my confidence daily.
        C G   C   G
Oh Ce - ci - lia, I'm down on my knees,
        C   G   D
I'm begging you please to come home.

Chorus 2

G   C   G
Celia, you're breaking my heart,
        C   G   D
You're shaking my confidence daily.
        C G   C   G
Oh Ce - ci - lia, I'm down on my knees,
        C   G   D G
I'm begging you please to come home, home.

Verse 1

                         C   G
Making love in the afternoon with Cecilia
C G   D G   C
Up in my bedroom, I got up to wash my face,
          G   D   G
When I come back to bed, someone's taken my place!

Chorus 3

G   C   G
Celia, you're breaking my heart,
        C   G   D
You're shaking my confidence daily.
        C G   C   G
Oh Ce - ci - lia, I'm down on my knees,
        C   G   D
I'm begging you please to come home,
        G
Come on home.

Instrumental   As Chorus 3

Verse 2

      (G) C G   **C**   **G**
Jub-i-la - tion, she loves me again,

     C   **G**   **D**
I fall on the floor and I'm laughing.

       C G   **C**   **G**
Jub-i-la - tion, she loves me again,

     C   **G**   **D**
I fall on the floor and I'm laughing.

Outro

          C G   **C**   **G**
‖: Woh oh, oh, oh oh, oh oh oh, oh,

      C   **G**   **D**
Woh, oh oh oh, oh oh oh, oh oh oh,

      C G   **C**   **G**
Woh oh, oh, oh oh, oh oh oh, oh,

      C   **G**   **D**
Woh, oh oh oh, oh oh oh, oh oh oh,:‖   *Repeat to fade*

Get Back

Words & Music by John Lennon & Paul McCartney

A   G   D

Intro | A | A | A | A G D ‖

Verse 1

A
Jo Jo was a man who thought he was a loner
D   **A**
But he knew it couldn't last.

Jo Jo left his home in Tucson, Arizona
D   **A**
For some California grass.

Chorus 1

A   **D**   **A**   **G** **D**
Get back, get back, get back to where you once belonged,
A   **D**   **A**
Get back, get back, get back to where you once belonged.

(Get back Jo Jo).

Instrumental | A | A | D | A G D ‖

Chorus 2

  A   **D**   **A**   **G** **D**
Get back, get back, get back to where you once belonged,
          A   **D**
Get back, get back, get back to where you once belonged.

(Get back Jo).

Instrumental | A | A | D | A G D ‖

Verse 2

A
Sweet Loretta Martin thought she was a woman
D   A
But.she was another man.

All the girls around her say she's got it coming
D   A G D
But she gets it while she can.

Chorus 3   As Chorus 1

Instrumental | A | A | D | A G D ‖

       A   D   A   G D
Chorus 4 Get back, get back, get back to where you once belonged,
       A   D
Get back, get back, get back to where you once belonged.

(Get back Jo).

       A   D
Coda   Get back Loretta,
(spoken)   A   G D
      Your Mommy is waiting for you

                         D
Wearin' her high-heeled shoes and her low neck sweater
          A G D
Get back home Loretta.

Chorus 5 ‖: As Chorus 1 :‖ *Repeat to fade*

21

Get It On (Bang A Gong)

Words & Music by Marc Bolan

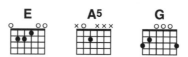

Verse 1

              E
Well you're dirty and sweet,

     A5   E
Clad in black, don't look back, and I love you,

     A5   E
You're dirty and sweet, oh yeah.

Well you're slim and you're weak,

          A5   E
You've got the teeth of the Hydra upon you,

     A5   E
You're dirty sweet and you're my girl.

Chorus 1

     G   A5   E
Get it on, bang a gong, get it on.

     G   A5   E
Get it on, bang a gong, get it on.

Verse 2

           (E)
Well you're built like a car,

        A5   E
You've got a hubcap diamond star halo,

     A5   E
You're built like a car, oh yeah.

                            A5
Well you're an untamed youth, that's the truth,

               E
With your cloak full of eagles

     A5   E
You're dirty sweet and you're my girl.

Chorus 2   As Chorus 1

Verse 3

          E
Well you're windy and wild
         A5   E
You've got the blues in your shoes and your stockings,
         A5   E
You're windy and wild, oh yeah.

Well you're built like a car,
         A5   E
You've got a hubcap diamond star halo,
         A5   E
You're dirty sweet and you're my girl.

Chorus 3   As Chorus 1

Instrumental ‖: E | E | E | E   :‖

               (E)
Verse 4   Well you're dirty and sweet,
         A5   E
Clad in black, don't look back, and I love you,
         A5   E
You're dirty and sweet, oh yeah.

Well you dance when you walk,
         A5   E
So let's dance, take a chance, understand me,
         A5   E
You're dirty sweet and you're my girl.

                 G   A5   E
Chorus 4 ‖: Get it on, bang a gong, get it on. :‖ *Play 3 times*

Instrumental ‖: E | E | E | E   :‖

                 G   A5   E
Chorus 5 ‖: Get it on, bang a gong, get it on. :‖ *Play 3 times*
          G   A5   E
Get it on, bang a gong, right on!
                 G   A   E
Take me!

Coda   Well meanwhile I'm still thinkin'.
(spoken)

I Still Haven't Found What I'm Looking For

Words & Music by U2

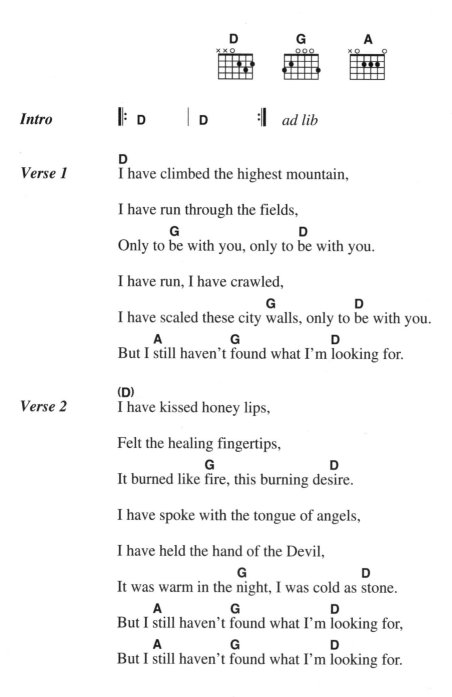

Intro ‖: D | D :‖ *ad lib*

Verse 1

D
I have climbed the highest mountain,

I have run through the fields,
G   **D**
Only to be with you, only to be with you.

I have run, I have crawled,
          G   **D**
I have scaled these city walls, only to be with you.
A   **G**   **D**
But I still haven't found what I'm looking for.

Verse 2

(D)
I have kissed honey lips,

Felt the healing fingertips,
      G   **D**
It burned like fire, this burning desire.

I have spoke with the tongue of angels,

I have held the hand of the Devil,
      G   **D**
It was warm in the night, I was cold as stone.
A   **G**   **D**
But I still haven't found what I'm looking for,
A   **G**   **D**
But I still haven't found what I'm looking for.

Instrumental |: D   G | D   G | D   G :|

            | G | G | D   G ||

Verse 3

D
I believe in the Kingdom Come

When all the colours will bleed into one,
         G   **D**
Bleed into one, but yes I'm still running.

You broke the bonds, loosed the chains,

Carried the cross and my shame,
       G
And my shame,
          D
You know I believe it.
     A   **G**   **D**
But I still haven't found what I'm looking for,
     A   **G**   **D**
But I still haven't found what I'm looking for.

I'm Still Remembering

Words & Music by Dolores O'Riordan

C   **Dm**   **Em**

Intro   ‖: C | Dm | Em | Dm :‖

Verse 1

    C   Dm   Em   Dm
I'm still remembering the day I gave my life away,

    C   Dm   Em   Dm
I'm still remembering the time you said you'd be mine.

    C   Dm   Em   Dm   C
Yesterday was cold and bare because you were not there,

    Dm   Em   Dm
Yesterday was cold, my story has been told.

Chorus 1

    C   Dm   Em   Dm
I need your affection all the way, _____

        C   Dm   Em   Dm
The weathers change or I'm changing the way. _____

    C   Dm   Em   Dm
I try to remain, I'm trying hard to go insane,

    C   Dm   Em   Dm
I need your affection all the way, the way.

        C   Dm   Em   Dm
Get away, get away, get away-ay-ay-ay-ay,

        C   Dm   Em   Dm
Get away, get away, get away-ay-ay-ay-ay.

Verse 2

    C   Dm   Em   Dm
I'm still remembering my life before I became your wife,

    C   Dm   Em   Dm
I'm still remembering the pain and mind-games.

    C   Dm   Em   Dm
Reverse psychology never tainted me,

    C   Dm   Em   Dm
I didn't sell my soul, I didn't sell my soul.

Chorus 2   As Chorus 1

Instrumental   ‖: C | Dm | Em | Dm   :‖

Verse 3
```
C              Dm            Em      Dm
They say the cream will always rise to the top,
C              Dm            Em          Dm
They say that good people are always the first to drop.
C                Dm          Em        Dm
What of Kurt Cobain, will his presence still remain?
    C         Dm     Em        Dm
Remember J.F.K. ever saintly in a way.
```

Bridge?
```
C           Dm  Em          Dm
Where are you now, where are you now?
C           Dm         Em          Dm
Where are you now, I said where are you now?
```

Outro
```
C            Dm          Em   Dm
I need your affection all the way, _____
C            Dm          Em   Dm
I need your affection all the way, _____
C            Dm          Em   Dm
I need your affection all the way, _____
C            Dm          Em   Dm
I need your affection all the way, _____
     C           Dm
All the way, all the way,
     Em          Dm
All the way, all the way,
     C           Dm
All the way, all the way,
     Em          Dm
All the way, all the way.
```

Instrumental   ‖: C | Dm | Em | Dm   :‖   *Repeat to fade*
(All the way.)

In The Air Tonight

Words & Music by Phil Collins

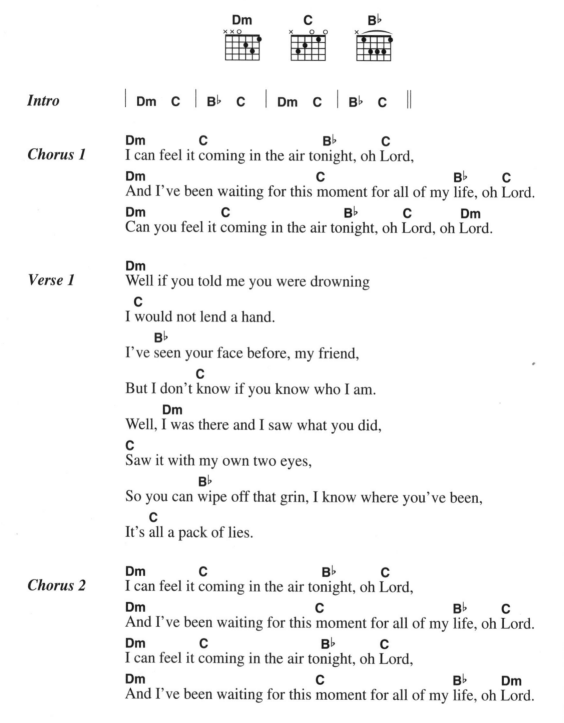

Intro

| Dm C | B♭ C | Dm C | B♭ C ||

Chorus 1

Dm   C   B♭   C
I can feel it coming in the air tonight, oh Lord,
Dm   C   B♭   C
And I've been waiting for this moment for all of my life, oh Lord.
Dm   C   B♭   C   Dm
Can you feel it coming in the air tonight, oh Lord, oh Lord.

Verse 1

Dm
Well if you told me you were drowning
  C
I would not lend a hand.
     B♭
I've seen your face before, my friend,
      C
But I don't know if you know who I am.
      Dm
Well, I was there and I saw what you did,
C
Saw it with my own two eyes,
        B♭
So you can wipe off that grin, I know where you've been,
     C
It's all a pack of lies.

Chorus 2

Dm   C   B♭   C
I can feel it coming in the air tonight, oh Lord,
Dm   C   B♭   C
And I've been waiting for this moment for all of my life, oh Lord.
Dm   C   B♭   C
I can feel it coming in the air tonight, oh Lord,
Dm   C   B♭   Dm
And I've been waiting for this moment for all of my life, oh Lord.

Verse 2

Dm
Well I remember, I remember, don't worry,

C   B♭
How could I ever forget the first time,

                        C
The last time we ever met.

              Dm
But I know the reason why you keep the silence up,

C
No you don't fool me.

              B♭
The hurt doesn't show, but the pain still grows,

                        Dm
It's no stranger to you or me.

Chorus 3

Dm   C   B♭   C
I can feel it coming in the air tonight, oh Lord,

Dm   C   B♭   C
And I've been waiting for this moment for all of my life, oh Lord.

Dm   C   B♭   C
I can feel it in the air tonight, oh Lord, oh Lord,

Dm   C   B♭   Dm
And I've been waiting for this moment for all of my life, oh Lord.

Coda

Dm   C   B♭   C
I can feel it coming in the air tonight, oh Lord,

Dm   C   B♭   C
Well I've been waiting for this moment all of my life, oh Lord.

Dm   C   B♭   C
I can feel it in the air tonight, oh Lord, oh Lord, oh Lord

Dm   C   B♭   C
And I've been waiting for this moment for all of my life, oh Lord. *Fade*

Jolene

Words & Music by Dolly Parton

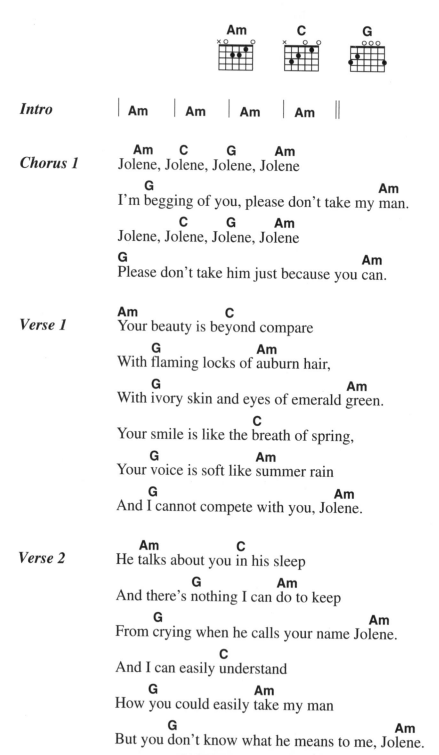

Intro | Am | Am | Am | Am ||

Chorus 1
Am   C   G   Am
Jolene, Jolene, Jolene, Jolene
        G   Am
I'm begging of you, please don't take my man.
        C   G   Am
Jolene, Jolene, Jolene, Jolene
G   Am
Please don't take him just because you can.

Verse 1
Am   C
Your beauty is beyond compare
        G   Am
With flaming locks of auburn hair,
        G   Am
With ivory skin and eyes of emerald green.
                        C
Your smile is like the breath of spring,
        G   Am
Your voice is soft like summer rain
        G   Am
And I cannot compete with you, Jolene.

Verse 2
Am   C
He talks about you in his sleep
              G   Am
And there's nothing I can do to keep
        G   Am
From crying when he calls your name Jolene.
                C
And I can easily understand
        G   Am
How you could easily take my man
        G   Am
But you don't know what he means to me, Jolene.

Chorus 2

      Am   **C**   **G**   **Am**
Jolene, Jolene, Jolene, Jolene

      G   **Am**
I'm begging of you, please don't take my man.

            C   **G**   **Am**
Jolene, Jolene, Jolene, Jolene

G   **Am**
Please don't take him just because you can.

Verse 3

Am   **C**
You could have your choice of men,

      G   **Am**
But I could never love again.

G   **Am**
He's the only one for me, Jolene.

                 C
I had to have this talk with you,

      G   **Am**
My happiness depends on you

       G   **Am**
And whatever you decide to do, Jolene.

Chorus 3   As Chorus 2

Julie

Words & Music by Simon Friend, Charles Heather, Mark Chadwick,
Jonathan Sevink & Jeremy Cunningham

Intro | D | G | D | G ||

Verse 1

D   G   D
Julie was a lonely girl, she said she was born that way,
                                    G
She'd always felt that way.
D   G   D
She left home at sixteen, got a job, what are you supposed to do?
                                    G
That's what you got to do.
D   G
She fell in love and settled down
                    D   G
In a council place there on the edge of town.
D   A   G   D   A   G
She'd feel alone in a crowded room, cry when she heard a happy tune.

Verse 2

            D   G   D
Well, it would be nice to holiday, till they took her job away,
                    G
They just took her life away.
D   G   D
Doing nothing isn't fun, when you've nothing from which to run,
                                    G
Yeah, you've nowhere left to run.
D   G   D
She'd visit the social every day, every time to be turned away,
                                    G
Every time to be turned away.
D   A   G   D   A   G
She'd feel alone in a crowded room, cry when she heard a happy tune.

Verse 3

     D   G   D

A hundred stairs to her new room, over glass and blackened spoons,

                          G

Children grow old so soon.

     D   G   D

Past the kids who gather there, pain masked by narcotic stares,

                          G

But no-one really cares.

     D   A   G

Her dreams were cut up and bled dry,

     D   A   G

Million voices in her cry.

 A   D   G   A

Julie waits, her world is her window,

                       D   G   A

And Julie hates just what she doesn't know,

                   D   G   A

And Julie hates, she hates the world below,

                   D   G   A

But Julie loves, she loves too much to know.

Common People

Music by Pulp. Lyrics by Jarvis Cocker

C   F   G

Intro | C | C | C | C   ‖

Verse 1

C
She came from Greece, she had a thirst for knowledge,

She studied sculpture at St. Martin's college,
G
That's where I caught her eye.
C
She told me that her dad was loaded,

I said "In that case I'll have rum and Coca Cola,"
G
She said "Fine."

And then in thirty seconds time she said
F
"I want to live like common people,
C
I want to do whatever common people do,

Want to sleep with common people,
G
I want to sleep with common people like you."

Well, what else could I do?
C
I said, "I'll... I'll see what I can do."

Verse 2

(C)
I took her to a supermarket,

                                                     G
I don't know why but I had to start it somewhere, so it started there.

C
  I said "Pretend you've got no money,"

                                                G
She just laughed and said "Oh, you're so funny," I said "Yeah?"

(Well I can't see anyone else smiling in here),

                      F
Are you sure? "You want to live like common people,

                                      C
You want to see whatever common people see,

You want to sleep with common people,

                                    G
You want to sleep with common people like me."

                                                      C
But she didn't understand, she just smiled and held my hand.

Verse 3

Rent a flat above a shop, cut your hair and get a job,

       G
Smoke some fags and play some pool, pretend you never went to school,

         C
But still you'll never get it right 'cause when you're laid in bed at night

       G
Watching 'roaches climb the wall,

If you called your dad he could stop it all, yeah.

F
  You'll never live like common people,

                                    C
You'll never do whatever common people do.

You'll never fail like common people,

                                  G
You'll never watch your life slide out of view,

And then dance and drink and screw

                    C
Because there's nothing else to do.

Instrumental ‖: C | C | C | C | G | G | G | G :‖

Verse 4

      F
Sing along with the common people,

                       C
Sing along and it might just get you through.

Laugh along with the common people,

                          G
Laugh along even though they're laughing at you

And the stupid things that you do,

              C
Because you think that poor is cool.

Verse 5

Like a dog lying in the corner,

They will bite you and never warn you,

G
Look out, they'll tear your insides out,

C
'Cause everybody hates a tourist,

                          G
Especially one who thinks it's all such a laugh,

And the chip stains and grease will come out in the bath.

        F
You will never understand how it feels to live your life

        C
With no meaning or control and nowhere left to go.

        G
You are amazed that they exist

                             C
And they burn so bright whilst you can only wonder why.

Verse 6   As Verse 3

| C | C | C | C | ‖

(C)
‖: Want to live with common people like you. :‖ *Play 7 times*

‖: Oh, la, la, la, la. :‖   *Play 4 times*

Oh yeah.

Lily The Pink

Traditional
Arranged & Adapted by John Gorman, Roger McGough & Mike McGear

C   G   G7

Chorus 1

          C   G
We'll drink a drink a drink to Lily the Pink the Pink the Pink
                       C
The saviour of the human race
                          G
For she invented medicinal compound
          G7   C
Most efficacious in every case.

Verse 1

   C   G
Mr Flears had sticking out ears
                  C
And it made him awful shy
                                G
And so she gave him medicinal compound
          G7   C
Now he's learning how to fly.

Verse 2

   C   G
Brother Tony was known to be boney
                    C
He would never eat his meals,
                               G
And so they gave him medicinal compound
          G7   C
Now they move him round on wheels.

Chorus 2   As Chorus 1

CONTINUED ON NEXT PAGE...

Verse 3

     C   G
Old Ebenezer thought he was Julius Caesar

         C
And so they put him in a home

              G
Where they gave him medicinal compound

        G7   C
And now he's the Emperor of Rome.

Verse 4

     C   G
Johnny Hammer had a terrible s. s. s. stammer,

           C
He could hardly s. s. say a w. w. word,

              G
And so they gave him medicinal compound

     G7   C
Now he's seen but never heard.

Chorus 3

We'll drink a drink a drink to Lily the Pink the Pink the Pink

The saviour of the human race

For she invented medicinal compound

Most efficacious in every case.

Verse 5

     C   G
Aunt Millie went willy nilly,

           C
When her legs they did recede,

             G
And so they rubbed on medicinal compound

       G7 C
Now they call her Millie Pede.

Verse 6

     C   G
Jennifer Eccles had terrible freckles

      G7   C
And the boys all called her names,

             G
But she changed with medicinal compound

      G7   C
Now she joins in all their games.

Chorus 4   As Chorus 3

Verse 7

     C   G
Lily the Pink she turned to drink she

                    C
Filled up with paraffin inside,

                    G
And despite her medicinal compound

    G7   C
Sadly pickled Lily died.

Verse 8
(slower)

     C   G
Up to heaven her soul ascended

                      C
Oh the church bells they did ring,

                    G
She took with her medicinal compound

    G7   C
Hark the herald angels sing.

Chorus 5

     C   G
We'll drink a drink a drink to Lily the Pink the Pink the Pink

                    C
The saviour of the human race

                    G
For she invented medicinal compound

    G7   C
Most efficacious in every case.

Lay Down Sally

Words & Music by Eric Clapton, Marcy Levy & George Terry

A   D   E

Intro   ‖: A | A | A | A :‖

Verse 1
A
There is nothing that is wrong
                                    D
In wanting you to stay here with me.
     A
I know you've got somewhere to go

But won't you make yourself at home
     D
And stay with me?
                    E
And don't you ever leave.

Chorus 1
A   D
Lay down Sally and rest you in my arms,
E   A
Don't you think you want someone to talk to?
                    D
Lay down Sally, no need to leave so soon,
E   A
I've been trying all night long just to talk to you.

Link | A | A | A | A ‖

Verse 2

     A
The sun ain't nearly on the rise

                                  D
And we still got the moon and the stars above.

     A
Underneath the velvet skies

Love is all that matters.

        D
Won't you stay with me?

           E
And don't you ever leave.

Chorus 2   As Chorus 1

Intro   ‖: A | A | A | A   :‖ *Ad lib*

     (A)
Verse 3   I long to see the morning light

                          D
Colouring your face so dreamily.

       A
So don't you go and say goodbye,

You can lay your worries down

       D
And stay with me

         E
And don't you ever leave.

Chorus 3   ‖: As Chorus 1 :‖   *Repeat to fade*

Love Me Do

Words & Music by John Lennon & Paul McCartney

G   C   D

Intro

| G | C | G | C |
| G | C | G | G ||

Verse 1

G   C
Love, love me do,
     G   C
You know I love you,
     G   C
I'll always be true,

So please _____
        G C G   C
Love me do, oh love me do.

Verse 2

G   C
Love, love me do,
     G   C
You know I love you,
     G   C
I'll always be true,

So please _____
        G C G
Love me do, oh love me do.

Bridge

D
Someone to love,
C   G
Somebody new,
D
Someone to love,
C   G
Someone like you.

Verse 3

G   C
Love, love me do,

   G   C
You know I love you,

  G   C
I'll always be true,

So please _____

       G C G
Love me do, oh love me do.

Instrumental ‖: D | D | C | G   :‖

         | G | G | G | G   ‖

Verse 4

G   C
Love, love me do,

   G   C
You know I love you,

  G   C
I'll always be true,

So please _____

       G C G   C
Love me do, oh love me do.

Coda

       G
Yeah, love me do,

C   G   C
Woh-oh love me do.   *(Fade)*

Memphis Tennessee

Words & Music by Chuck Berry

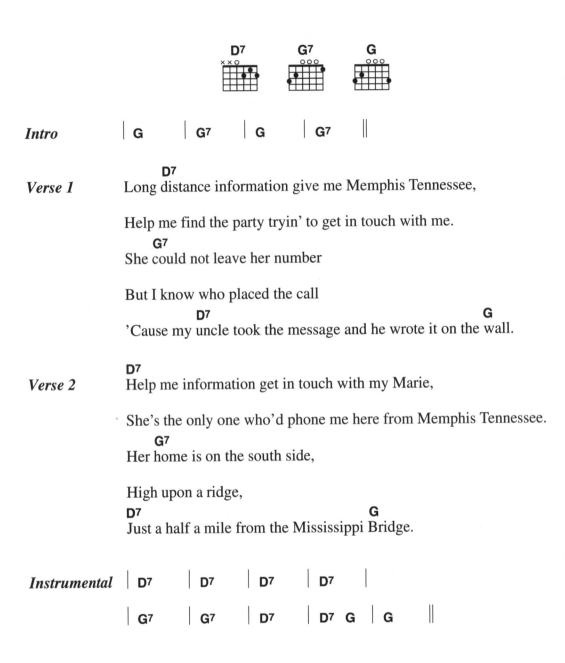

Intro | G | G7 | G | G7 ||

Verse 1
       D7
Long distance information give me Memphis Tennessee,

Help me find the party tryin' to get in touch with me.
  G7
She could not leave her number

But I know who placed the call
      D7   **G**
'Cause my uncle took the message and he wrote it on the wall.

Verse 2
D7
Help me information get in touch with my Marie,

  She's the only one who'd phone me here from Memphis Tennessee.
  G7
Her home is on the south side,

High upon a ridge,
D7   **G**
Just a half a mile from the Mississippi Bridge.

Instrumental | D7 | D7 | D7 | D7 |

| G7 | G7 | D7 | D7 G | G ||

Verse 3

          D7
Help me information, more than that I cannot add,

Only that I miss her and all the fun we had,
           G7
But we were pulled apart

Because her Mom did not agree
           D7   **G**
And tore apart our happy home in Memphis Tennessee.

Verse 4

          D7
The last time I saw Marie she's waving me goodbye

With hurry-home drops on her cheek that trickled from her eye,
          G7
Marie is only six years old,

Information please,
D7   **G**
Try to put me through to her in Memphis Tennessee.

Mersey Paradise

Words & Music by Ian Brown & John Squire

D   G   A

Intro | D | D | G A | G A ‖

Verse 1

D
River splashes against the rocks
    G   **A**   **G**   **A**
And I scale the slope and hope the tracks
    D
Won't lead me down to dark black pits
    G   **A**   **G**   **A**
Or places where we fall to bits.

Verse 2

    D
If she were there I'd hold her down,
    G   **A**   **G**   **A**
I'll push her under while she drowns
    D
And couldn't breathe and call for air,
    G   **A**   **G**   **A**
She doesn't care for my despair.

Chorus 1

    G   **D**   **G**
Or is it me? Or the one that's wrong?
A
You see in this heat
    D   **G**
River cools where I belong
A   **D**
In my Mersey paradise.

| G | D | G | A | G A ‖

Verse 3

     D
As I stare an oil wheel comes
     G   **A** **G**   **A**
Sailing by and I feel like
     D
Growing fins and falling in
          G   **A**   **G**   **A**
With the bricks, the bikes, the rusty tins.

Verse 4

     D
I swim along without a care,
       G   **A**   **G**   **A**
I'm eating sand when I need air.
         D
You can bet your life I'll meet a pike
      G   **A**   **G**   **A**
Who'll wolf me down for tea tonight.

Chorus 2

A   **G**   **D**
I want to be (I want to be),
              G
Where the drownings are (drownings are).
A   **G**
You see in this heat
        D   **G**
River cools where I belong,
A   **D**
In my Mersey Paradise.

Solo   ‖: **D** | **D** | **G** **A** | **G** **A** :‖

Chorus 3

A   **G**   **D**
I want to be (I want to be),
              G   **A**
Where the drownings are (drownings are).
         G
You see in this heat
        D   **G**
River cools where I belong.

Chorus 4   As Chorus 2

Rivers Of Babylon

Words & Music by Farian, Reyam, Dowe & McNaughton

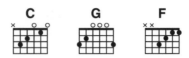

Intro

               C
(Ah ah ah ah, ah ah ah ah,
      G   **C**
Ah ah ah ah, ah ah ah ah ah.)

Chorus 1

                 C
‖: By the rivers of Babylon there we sat down
      G   **C**
Yeah we wept when we remembered Zion. :‖

Verse 1

               C
‖: For the wicked carried us away in captivity,
   F   **C**
Require from us a song.

Now how shall we sing the Lord's song
      G   **C**
In a strange land? :‖

Instrumental   As Intro

Verse 2

           C   **G**
‖: Let the words of our mouths
               C   **G**
And the meditation of our hearts
       C   **G**
Be acceptable in Thy sight
     C
Here tonight. :‖

Chorus 2

                 C
‖: By the rivers of Babylon there we sat down
      G   **C**
Yeah we wept when we remembered Zion. :‖ *Repeat to fade*

1/05 (53560)